Jamie's Journal

All photographs have come from the *Cook with Jamie* shoot.

MICHAEL JOSEPH

Published by the Penguin Group
Penguin Books Ltd, 80 Strand, London WC2R 0RL, England
Penguin Group (USA) Inc., 375 Hudson Street, New York, New York 10014, USA
Penguin Group (Canada), 90 Eglinton Avenue East, Suite 700, Toronto, Ontario, Canada M4P 2Y3
(a division of Pearson Penguin Canada Inc.)
Penguin Ireland, 25 St Stephen's Green, Dublin 2, Ireland (a division of Penguin Books Ltd)
Penguin Group (Australia), 250 Camberwell Road,
Camberwell, Victoria 3124, Australia (a division of Pearson Australia Group Pty Ltd)
Penguin Books India Pvt Ltd, 11 Community Centre,
Penguin Group (NZ), 67 Apollo Drive, Mairangi Bay, Auckland 1310, New Zealand
(a division of Pearson New Zealand Ltd)
Penguin Books (South Africa) (Pty) Ltd, 24 Sturdee Avenue,
Rosebank, Johannesburg 2196, South Africa

Penguin Books Ltd, Registered Offices: 80 Strand, London WC2R 0RL, England

www.penguin.com

This edition produced for The Book People Ltd, Hall Wood Avenue, Haydock, St Helens, WA11 9UL
First published 2006
1

Copyright © Jamie Oliver, 2006
Photographs copyright © David Loftus and Chris Terry, 2006

The moral right of the author has been asserted

Colour Reproduction by Dot Gradations Ltd, UK
Printed and bound in Italy by L.E.G.O.

A CIP catalogue record for this book is available from the British Library

ISBN-10: 0-718-15288-3
ISBN-13: 978-0-718-15288-8

Top gear that makes a difference in the kitchen

Here's a list of some of the things that, for me, make a real difference in the kitchen. They're bits of equipment that I use every day and help me make better, tastier food. I promise they won't end up gathering dust in the back of the cupboard!

Before everything else, I want to talk to you about your hob. Most people forget that it's one of the most essential things in a kitchen! Great cooking starts with the best heat source – and gas is where it's at. It gives off a more predictable heat than ceramic or electric hobs, it's easier to control and you can see exactly what's going on. So if you're a proper cook, get yourself a gas hob.

Speed peeler
A good-quality U-shaped speed peeler is a godsend in the kitchen, whether you're peeling veg, shaving Parmesan or finely slicing fennel or asparagus. Quick and precise, it's a genius piece of kit.

Tongs
Tongs give better control when grilling or turning meat on the barbecue and are great for picking up hot things and for serving food.

Flavour Shaker and pestle and mortar
A pestle and mortar is my ultimate kitchen gadget, but sometimes its size and weight can be off-putting. A Flavour Shaker is a modern, downsized version of a pestle and mortar and is really user-friendly. Both will help you bash and bruise and get the flavour out of loads of ingredients.

Knives
At home I have three knives that I use all the time when cooking: an 8-inch chef's knife, a small vegetable paring knife and a serrated carving knife. You should also invest in a trusty steel to keep them sharp. Don't use a steel on serrated knives though, it'll ruin the blade.

Food processor
I love mine! Food processors help you chop, mix and purée ingredients, saving you loads of time – cooking becomes a doddle.

A big pot
A very large, thick-bottomed cooking pot is really useful for dinner parties, curries, stews and cooking big batches. Every house should have one. And I'm not talking about big, but double big.

Non-stick frying pans
Great ones have a good non-stick coating, a nice thick bottom and an ovenproof handle. I think it's worth investing in a few different sizes as they can be used for so many things. Remember to use wooden spoons – they're much kinder on the non-stick surface. Hang them, don't stack them, and they'll stay in great nick.

Good-quality grater
There are some fantastic high-tech graters out there these days. They're perfect for zesting fruit and grating all sorts of things from chocolate to cheese to nutmeg. Be careful with your fingers though, they can be extremely sharp.

Salad spinner
Many people don't quite get it, but salad spinners are incredibly important for making wicked salads. After washing your salad leaves, you don't want any water clinging to the leaves, otherwise they'll be tasteless and the dressing won't stick. So get spinning!

Nest of mixing bowls
I want you to really go for it with these and get a whole selection – either cheap metal ones or porcelain ones. You'll use them all the time for mixing, marinating and storing stuff in the fridge. Look out for ones with handy measurements on the inside surface.

Chopping board
Try and get your hands on a thick wooden chopping board. They're quite expensive (maybe you can ask for one for your birthday!), but you'll be using it for the rest of your life and it will age beautifully along with you. Slightly less glamorous but still essential is a plastic chopping board for fish and meat that fits in your dishwasher.

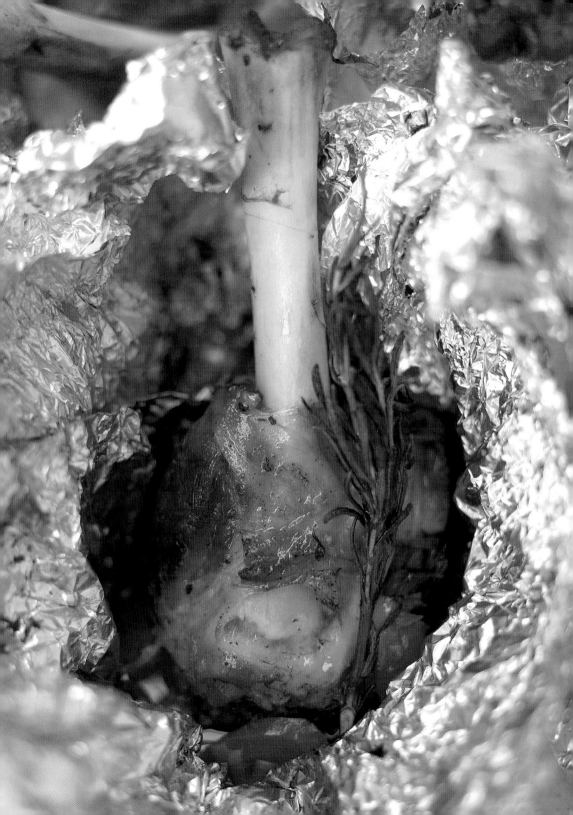